THE DAILY ROAR
SCOOP!
NO BULL! ROAR DEAL FOR EDITOR EXPOSED AS MEMBER OF THE "FAKE PERSON CLUB"
Top reporter, Monty Molenski, takes the bull by the horns!
THIS IS IT! MY BIG CHANCE FOR A SCOOP!

GRAND HOTEL

SECONDS LATER I WAS OUTSIDE THE HOTEL.
SECURITY WAS TIGHT: A CLEAR SIGN
THEY MUST BE UP TO NO GOOD.
THE DOORMAN DIDN'T BUDGE AN
INCH WHEN I SHOWED HIM MY PRESS
PASS, THE BIG KNUCKLEHEAD!

I'm Quentin
'Happy to help!'

PRIVATE PARTY
Strictly
embers ONLY

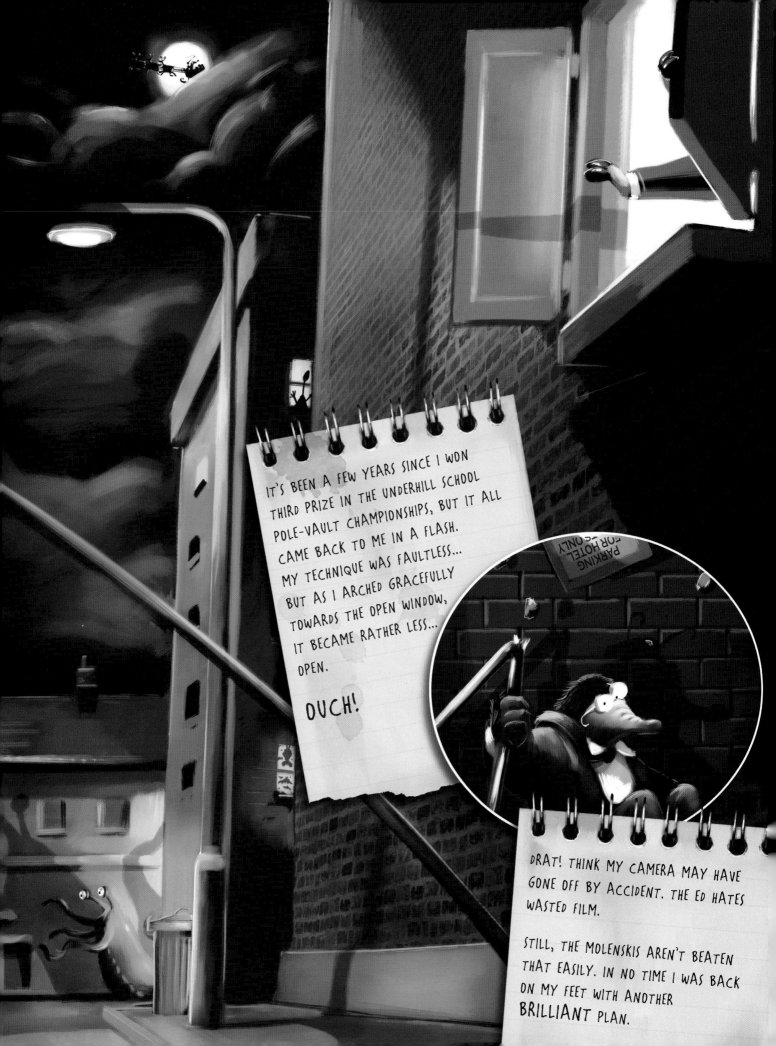

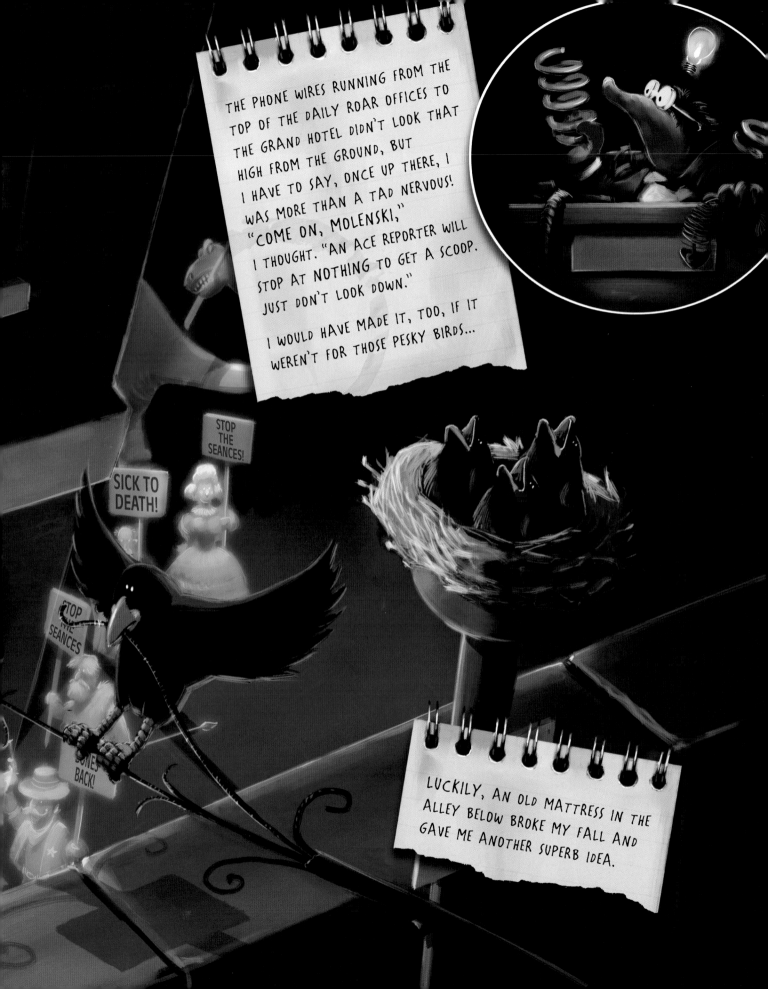

GRAND HOTEL

click!

BACK ON THE ROOF OF THE DAILY ROAR, I TOOK A DEEP BREATH AND LAUNCHED MYSELF INTO SPACE WEARING MY NEW 'GRAVITY-DEFYING MOLENSKI SPRING-BOOTS'. UNFORTUNATELY, THE SPRINGS WERE A TEEEEEENSY BIT MORE POWERFUL THAN I'D CALCULATED. INSTEAD OF LANDING ON THE ROOF OF THE GRAND HOTEL, I OVERSHOT IT RATHER, AND ALMOST ENDED UP IN THE BOATING LAKE.

IT'S GOING TO BE A LONG WALK BACK.

TRUDGING BACK, I WAS ALMOST
READY TO GIVE UP, BUT THEN THE
MOLENSKI FAMILY MOTTO CAME
TO MIND: "IF AT FIRST YOU DON'T
SUCCEED, DIG A LITTLE DEEPER".
OF COURSE! THAT WAS MY WAY IN!
RUSHING DOWN TO THE BASEMENT OF
THE DAILY ROAR, I BEGAN TO DIG
FURIOUSLY.
MY NATURAL BURROWING INSTINCTS
SERVED ME WELL AND I DUG LIKE A
MOLE POSSESSED, HEADING STRAIGHT
AND TRUE FOR THE BASEMENT OF THE
GRAND HOTEL.

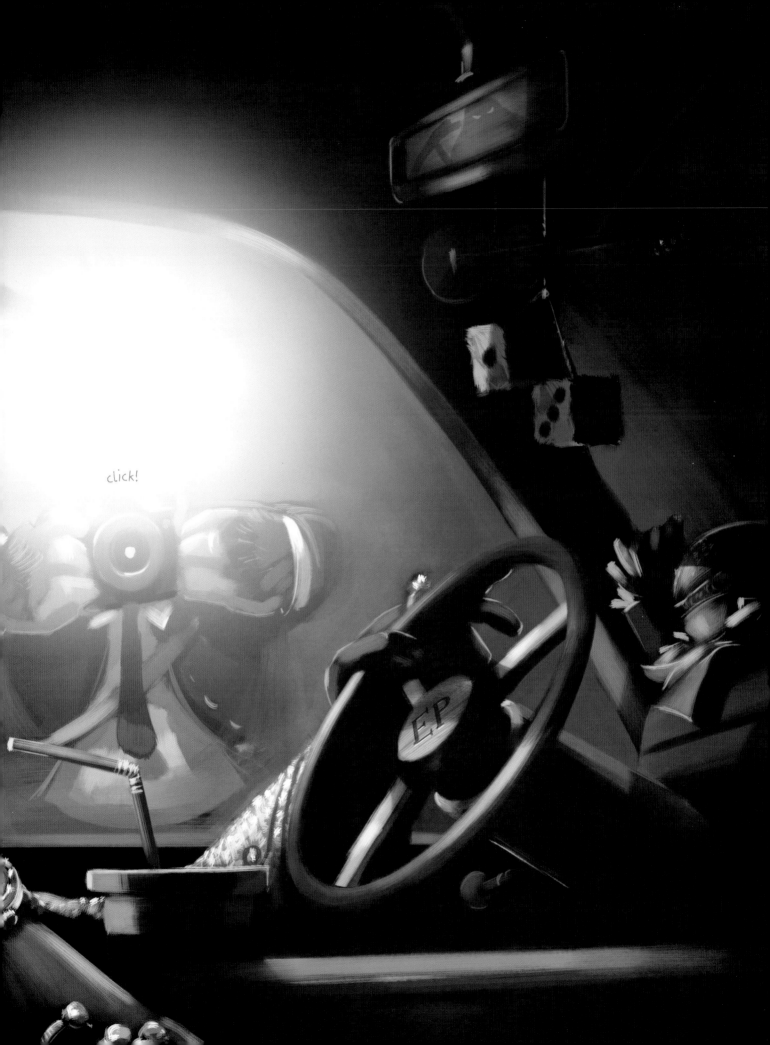
click!

DARKROOM
THE DAILY ROAR
ALL CAMERAS MUST BE LEFT HERE FOR OVERNIGHT PROCESSING
-THE NITE OWL
THOROUGHLY FED UP. RETURNED TO THE DESERTED DAILY ROAR OFFICES TO DROP OFF MY CAMERA AT THE NITE OWL'S FILM DEVELOPMENT LAB AS USUAL.
WHAT A WASTE OF TIME. OH, WELL. HOME TO BED.

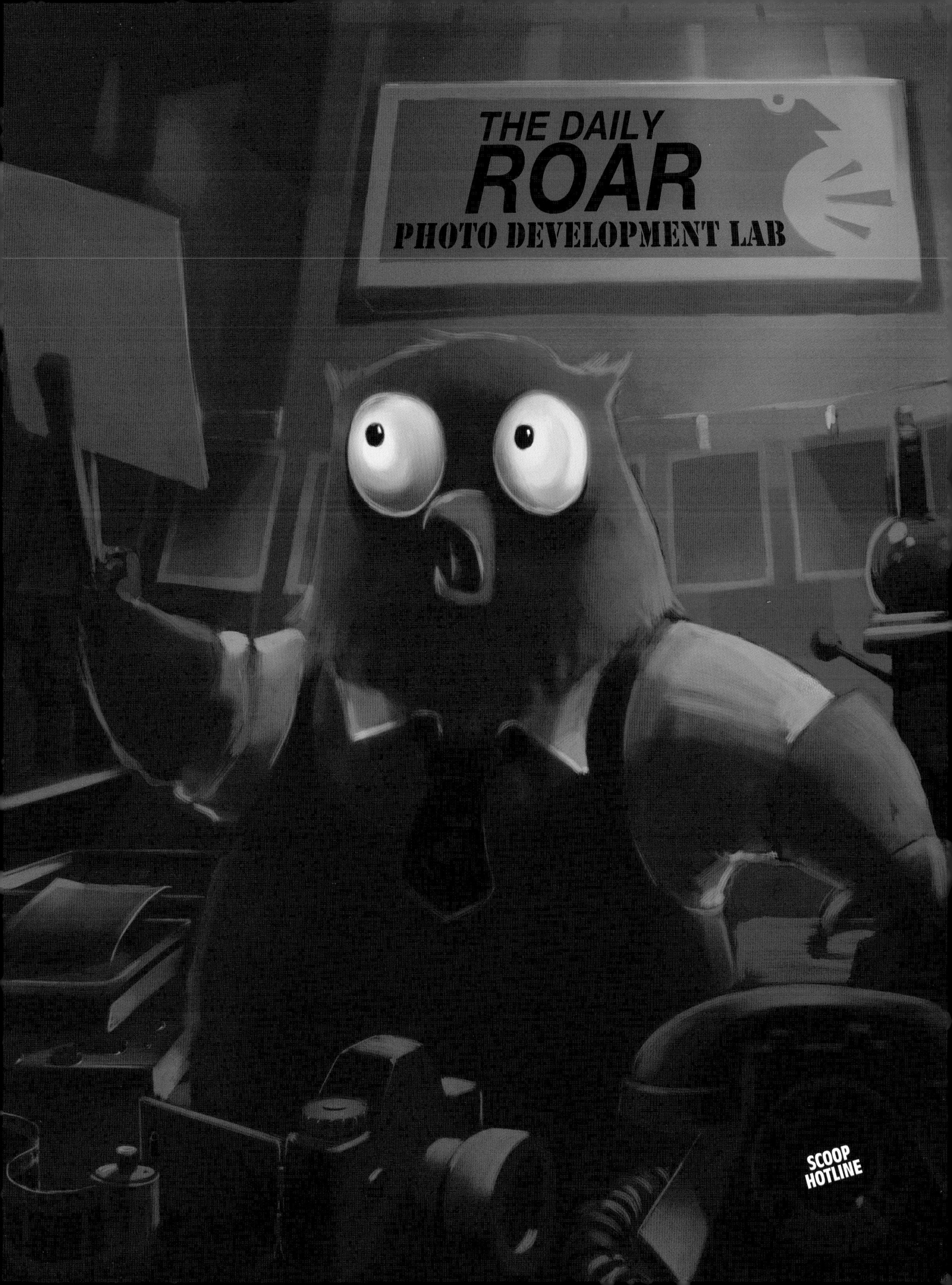
THE DAILY
ROAR
PHOTO DEVELOPMENT LAB
SCOOP
HOTLINE

MONDAY.
AMAZING. SEEMS LIKE I GOT SOME INTERESTING SHOTS AFTER ALL. WELL, OF COURSE, I ALWAYS KNEW I WOULD. THE MOLENSKI INVESTIGATIVE ANTENNA NEVER REALLY STOPS WORKING. THE PAPER'S SELLING LIKE CRAZY.

THE DAILY ROAR

SCOOP!

WRONG-FOOTED!
BIGFOOT
BROUGHT TO HEEL
By our reporter, Monty Molenski

THE DAILY ROAR

SCOOP!

HI SPIRITS!
GHOSTS BUSTED
An EXCLUSIVE by ace reporter, Monty Molenski

WE'RE SICK TO DEATH!

GIVE OUR BONES BACK!

GIVE BO BA

TUESDAY.
AT LAST, I'M OFFICIALLY 'ACE' REPORTER AT THE DAILY ROAR.
ABOUT TIME!

WEDNESDAY.
THE NATIONAL PAPERS ARE CALLING ME 'REPORTER OF THE CENTURY'! MY PHONE HASN'T STOPPED RINGING AND I'M GOING TO BE ON TELLY TONIGHT! (MUST GET MUM TO SET THE VIDEO.)

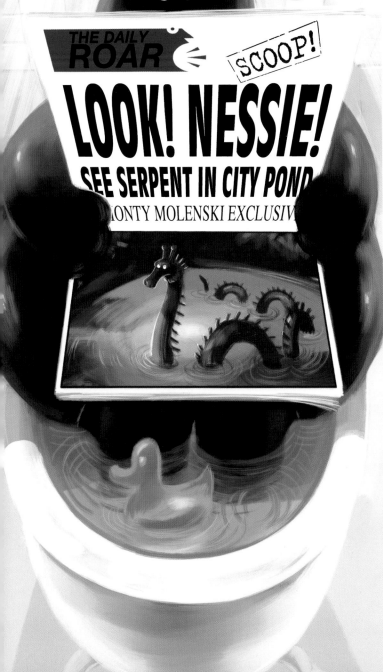

THE DAILY ROAR

SCOOP!

LOOK! NESSIE!
SEE SERPENT IN CITY POND
MONTY MOLENSKI EXCLUSIVE

THE DAILY ROAR

SCOOP!

BY MOLENSKI THE KING AND I — ELVIS LIVES!
Suspicious minds proved correct

BY M
THE K
ELVI
Suspicious

THURSDAY.
THEY'RE GOING TO MAKE A FILM OF MY LIFE!